Table of Contents

To the Teacher

This book is part of the Creative Expressions in Mythology Series. It contains a series of mythology stories with each having a vocabulary lesson, discussion questions, creative questions and extra activities that involve creative writing, designs or projects.

DIRECTIONS:

Step 1: Begin the unit by introducing the vocabulary words on the vocabulary activity sheet. (These words are underlined in the stories.) Ask the students to look up the definitions and write them on their sheets. Many of the vocabulary lessons include a section where the student must use the vocabulary words to write a brief paragraph about the story. This will need to be completed after reading the myth.

Step 2: Read the myth, individually or together, and use the comprehension/discussion questions to talk about the story. The vocabulary lesson sheet can be completed now if it involves a writing activity.

Step 3: The students are now ready to complete the creative questions. These questions are all asked at the upper levels of Bloom's Taxonomy. The questions are designed to encourage students to think at a higher level and not just repeat information learned in the story. Many of the questions involve no right or wrong answers; therefore, grading will be subjective. I suggest that you look for creative answers using knowledge gained from the myth.

Step 4: When the creative questions have been answered, you may let students pick out one or all of the extra activities. These activities include creative writing, illustrating, design or creating something new that will support the myth. These can be assigned or done for extra credit.

Step 5: After reading some or all the myths, students can participate in the research-project unit. Directions are given.

The objectives of this book are to encourage students to learn about mythology, to use the acquired learning and to develop something new through a research project. In today's society, research is so important for the students. The skills needed to complete research will be used through college and careers. Educators must give students the skills to successfully complete research beginning in elementary school. Through the use of this book, opportunities will be made available for students to produce a project that will bring satisfaction to them and the teacher.

Introduction

The Greek civilization began more than 2,000 years ago. At that time Greece controlled land bordering the Mediterranean and Black seas. As with most ancient civilizations, people tried to explain the mysteries of nature and how things came to be, so they created gods and goddesses. These powerful beings were believed to rule the sky, the seas, the earth and the underworld. They played an important part in the people's lives. These stories came to be known as myths. The myths of ancient Greece told of Mount Olympus, a mountain too high for mortals to climb. This was home for the gods. The people's belief in the gods was so strong that temples were built in their honor. Sacrifices and gifts were offered in these temples, hoping the gods would look on them favorably.

Throughout history these myths grew and changed as they were told and retold. This book revisits some of the more popular versions of Greek myths. They deal with not only with the gods and goddesses but also with life and death, the exploits of heroes and the dealing of mortals with the gods. Keep in mind, however, that in many cases there are several versions of the same myth.

Creative Experiences in Greek Mythology includes ten myths. Following each story is vocabulary practice, comprehension and discussion questions, creative-thinking questions and other creative activities. At the end of the book is a research project.

Greek Mythology has always been an exciting, but imaginary way to explain the mysteries of life and death. I hope you will enjoy discovering the mysteries of Greek Mythology through the study of this book.

The Beginning

Greece, like many early civilizations had its own beliefs about how life began. According to Greek legends there was Chaos, a state of being not defined, a mass of whirling nothing without shape or form. From this Chaos emerged Mother Earth. She had a son named Uranus. He fashioned earth, flowers, trees, animals and birds. Mother Earth then gave birth to three-headed giants, and three one-eyed Cyclopes. Uranus was not happy with the Cyclopes so he cast them down to the Underworld. This upset Mother Earth. Even though she was angered by Uranus, she bore him twelve children, six sons and six daughters. These children became known as the Titans.

Mother Earth did not forget what Uranus did to the Cyclopes. She encouraged the Titans to rebel against Uranus. Cronus, Uranus' son, attacked and mortally wounded him with a flint scythe as he slept. Three drops of blood fell from his wounds and hit Mother Earth. These three drops of blood formed the three Furies. They retreated to the Underworld where they made their home.

After the death of Uranus, Cronus and his wife, Rhea, ruled the Titans. Before his death, Uranus had predicted that one of Cronus' own sons would overthrow him and become the ruler. This caused Cronus to be fearful that the prophecy might come true; therefore, each time Rhea bore him a child, he swallowed it before the baby opened its eyes. This made Rhea very angry.

The next time Rhea was ready to give birth, she hid in the mountains and Zeus was born. Rhea kept him hidden in caves where he was cared for by nymphs. The survival of Zeus led to the era of the new gods. The Titans, however, didn't disappear. They lived on into the new age with their sons and daughters. Old scores were yet to be settled.

Cronus found that Rhea had deceived him by hiding Zeus. He and his followers searched for Zeus. Even though the nymphs were doing their best to hide Zeus, Rhea knew Cronus would eventually find him. She devised a plan to trick Cronus. She wrapped a rock in swaddling clothes and presented it to Cronus as Zeus. He immediately swallowed the stone. Cronus thought he was safe, so he called off his search for Zeus.

Zeus grew to manhood. Rhea would visit him in the cave, telling him what Cronus had done to his brothers and sisters. Zeus was determined to rescue his siblings. Rhea and Zeus visited the Metis, a Titaness who was very wise, and asked for advice on how to rescue his brothers and sisters.

After hearing her, Rhea presented Zeus to Cronus as a new cup-bearer. Cronus learned to trust Zeus. Later Zeus mixed a potion in Cronus's wine. It made him very sick. He vomited out Zeus's brothers and sisters: Hades, Poseidon, Demeter, Hera and Hesta. Now free, the children of Cronus were eager to get revenge. Poseidon and Hades persuaded Zeus to lead a rebellion against the Titans who supported Cronus.

The war between the old and new gods lasted many years. Zeus was encouraged to ask the one-eyed Cyclopes for help. Zeus traveled to the Underworld, where Cronus had imprisoned the Cyclopes, and set them free. In return they gave Zeus and his brothers three gifts: a thunderbolt for Zeus; a trident for Poseidon; and a helmet for Hades, which made him invisible.

The three formed a plan to destroy Cronus by using their gifts from the Cyclopes. Hades, wearing his helmet, stole into his room and took his weapons. When Cronus discovered that his weapons were missing, Poseidon came in and threatened him with his three-pronged trident. Zeus stalked up behind Cronus and struck him down with his thunderbolt. Cronus was killed instantly.

Cronus's death caused the defeat of the other Titans. All but two were banished to Tartarus, the worst section of the Underworld. Cronus was allowed to live in the Elysian Fields, a happier part of the Underworld. Atlas, the war leader, was made to hold the weight of the heavens on his shoulders forever

Zeus was now ready to create mankind. First he created men of the Golden Age. These men would laugh and sing all day. All their needs were provided for them. They ate fruit, honey, berries, nuts and milk from goats and sheep. They never had to work. They lived happily until their death. They would eventually die and their spirits would roam the earth, watching over later generations.

Next Zeus created men of the Silver Age. These men were dull witted, not far from being animals. They refused to make sacrifices to the gods and quarreled all the time. Zeus realized they would never change and destroyed them.

Zeus created the Bronze-Age men next. They were more intelligent, but just wanted to create weapons and fight. They cared nothing for beauty and useful things. They fought each other constantly until they were all destroyed.

Zeus's failures were discouraging. He decided to try one more time and created men of the Heroic Age. These men are discussed in many Greek legends. Two of these heroes were Jason, known for his adventures searching for the Golden Fleece, and Odysseus.

Men of the Heroic Age provided hours of entertainment for the gods and goddesses. They loved to get involved in mortals' lives and often helped protect a chosen hero. The gods and goddesses often took on mortal forms so they could move freely among mankind.

There were rules that humans had to follow when dealing with the gods. Most important was the rule that one could not challenge a god's supremacy. The gods were very jealous of someone who might overcome them. When this happened, the outcome was not usually good for the mortal.

The Beginning
Vocabulary Activities

Look up each word in the dictionary and write its definition.

Cyclops (Cyclopes, pl.)

scythe:

nymph(s)

swaddling:

siblings:

prophecy:

Fill in the blanks with a form of the correct vocabulary word from above.

1. The mother used _____ clothes to keep her child still.

2. The _____ foretold coming events.

3. The farmer was in the field with his _____ cutting grass.

4. She had three _____ and they fought all the time.

5. The _____ ran free through the forest.

6. The one-eyed _____ was very stubborn.

Use each vocabulary word in a paragraph about "The Beginning" according to the mythology of the ancient Greeks.

The Beginning
Comprehension Questions

1. Describe the beginning of life according to the Greek version.

_____

_____

_____

_____

2. Who were the Titans?

_____

_____

_____

_____

3. Rhea had a problem with Cronus. What was that problem?

_____

_____

_____

_____

4. How was Zeus saved from the same fate as his brothers and sisters?

_____

_____

_____

_____

5. Describe Zeus's attempts at creating mankind.

_____

_____

_____

_____

Answers to "The Beginning"
Comprehension Questions and Vocabulary Exercises

Discussion Questions

1. Describe the beginning of life according to the Greek version.

From Chaos came Mother Earth. She had a son who made the earth, flowers, trees, animals and birds.

2. Who were the Titans?

The Titan were the original gods and goddesses, sons and daughters of Mother Earth and Uranus.

3. Rhea had a problem with Cronus. What was that problem?

He swallowed each of her children as they were born because he feared one of them dethroning him.

4. How was Zeus saved from the same fate as his brothers and sisters?

His mother hid him in a cave where he grew up. She tricked Cronus into thinking that he had swallowed Zeus.

5. Describe Zeus's attempts at creating mankind.

He first created men of the Golden Age. They seemed to live a good life. Next he created men of the Silver Age. They were lazy and dumb. He destroyed them. He then created men of the Bronze Age. All they wanted to do was fight so he destroyed them, also. Lastly he created men of the Heroic Age. They lived to entertain and please the gods.

Look up each word in the dictionary and write its definition.

Cyclopes: giant beings with a single, round eye in the middle of their foreheads.

scythe: a tool that has a curved blade on a long curved handle and is used for mowing grass or grain by hand.

nymphs: goddesses in old legends represented as beautiful young girls living in mountains, forests, meadows, and waters

swaddling: narrow strips of cloth wrapped around an infant to restrict movement

siblings: one of two or more individuals having the same parents or sometimes only one parent in common

prophecy: the sayings of a prophet, foretelling of the future

Fill in the blanks with the correct vocabulary word.

1. The mother used <u>swaddling</u> clothes to keep her child still.
2. The <u>prophecy</u> foretold coming events.
3. The farmer was in the field with his <u>scythe</u> cutting grass.
4. She had three <u>siblings</u> and they fought all the time.
5. The <u>nymphs</u> ran free through the forest.
6. The one-eyed <u>Cyclops</u> was very stubborn.

The Beginning
Creative-Thinking Questions

1. Compare the beginning in Greek legends to the beginning according to Judeo-Christian beliefs or the beliefs of another culture. How are they alike and how are they different?

_____

_____

_____

_____

2. If you had been Cronus, how might you have handled the prophecy about being overthrown by one of your children differently?

_____

_____

_____

_____

3. How do you think Rhea convinced Zeus to overthrow his father?

_____

_____

_____

_____

4. Predict how Zeus might have rescued the Cyclopes.

_____

_____

_____

_____

5. Judge the gifts the Cyclopes gave each of the three gods.

_____

_____

_____

_____

6. Why do you think Cronus was sent to the Elysian Fields rather than Tartarus?

_____

_____

_____

_____

7. If you had a choice of which of Zeus' mankind to live in, which one would you choose and why?

_____

_____

_____

_____

8. Was it wise to challenge a god? Why or why not?

_____

_____

_____

_____

The Beginning
YOU ARE ZEUS

Pretend to be Zeus. Write about some of the conflicts you might
have had when fighting the Titans.

The Beginning
IT'S THE LAW!

Write about some of the laws Zeus might have
written for the other gods and goddesses.

The Beginning
FOR SALE!

Develop an advertisement that might be found in The Mount Olympus News.

The Beginning
READ ALL ABOUT IT!

Write a newspaper article for the Mount Olympus News about the creation of man according to Greek legends. Create a catchy headline.

Zeus, the Supreme God, and His Queen, Hera

Zeus was the ruling god of Olympus, which was located on the highest mountain in the world. Life for the gods and goddesses was good. They would look down upon earth and watch the mortals. Man would give sacrifices of meat for them to eat. They would drink sweet nectar from their goblets and listen to Apollo fill the air with his music.

Zeus ruled the gods, goddesses and mankind with the help of Destiny's wise counseling. Through Destiny, Zeus could see everything and know everything. Zeus was <u>compassionate</u> in his dealings with the weak, but he punished wrongdoers. He was worshiped as the god of the sky and lord of the winds, rain and thunder.

Zeus took Hera as his wife. She was not his first wife. Metis, the Titan, followed by Themis, Mnemosyne and Eurynome were Zeus' other wives. Themis gave birth to Peace, Justice and the three Fates. The Fates planned each mortal's life. Even after Themis was no longer Zeus' wife, she was allowed to remain in Olympus because he valued her advice. Hera was in agreement with this decision.

Zeus won Hera's hand in marriage by pretending to be a half-frozen cuckoo. She picked him up and warmed him against her chest. He resumed his normal form and she still loved him. Their marriage was a great event. Mother Earth gave Hera a tree that bore golden apples. Hera bore Zeus three children: Ares, god of war; Hephaestus, the smith god; and Hebe, the goddess of youth.

Because Zeus seemed too powerful for all the gods and goddesses, Hera decided to teach him a lesson. She convinced several other gods to help her. They seized Zeus and tied him up with ropes that contained hundreds of knots. This made Zeus very angry. He was helpless against the knots. The other gods <u>taunted</u> him, discussing which one would take his place. Zeus knew that he must escape or he would be <u>supplanted</u> just as his father had been.

No matter how much he tried, Zeus could not free himself. Thetis, the sea nymph, felt sorry for Zeus and brought the hundred-handed giant Briareus to help him. In no time, Zeus was free. His revenge was great. He sent Poseidon and Apollo across the seas to help build the walls of Troy for King Laomedon. Hera received the worst punishment. She was hung from the sky.

Each god had to swear an oath to never rebel against Zeus again. Only after this was done did Zeus let Hera go. Hera learned her lesson well. She always respected her husband's power from that point on.

Even though Hera and Zeus were married, they continued to fight. He constantly schemed to deceive her and go about his adventures. Hera usually found out what Zeus was up to and she opposed him, careful not to push him too far. She always remembered her punishment.

Hera became so angry with one of Zeus's adventures that she left him and moved to an island. Zeus could not stand to lose her so he tried to convince her to return to Olympus. She would not listen to him. He made a plan to bring Hera back. He dressed a statue so that it appeared to be a beautiful girl with a <u>coronet</u> of pearls on her head. He put the statue in a chariot and had it driven around the island while having <u>heralds</u> proclaim that she was to be his new bride. When Hera saw this, she quickly tore the clothes off the statue and realized she had been tricked. Because of her actions, her true feelings were shown. She had no choice but to return to Zeus.

Hera was wise and considerate when she wasn't angry with Zeus. She helped many mortals overcome obstacles. One such mortal was Jason, whom she helped return safely from his <u>perilous</u> journey in search of the Golden Fleece.

Zeus and Hera
Vocabulary Activities

Look up each word in the dictionary and write its definition.

Compassionate:

Taunted:

Supplanted:

Coronet:

Heralds:

Perilous:

Fill in the blanks with a form of the correct vocabulary word from above.

1. He was _____ by his brother.

2. She wore a _____ on her head.

3. We were warned that the situation was _____..

4. The boys _____ the poor dog

5.She was announced by the _____ and they fought all the time.

6. She felt _____ toward the hungry kitten, so she fed it.

Write a synonym for each vocabulary word.

Compassionate:

Taunted:

Supplanted:

Coronet:

Heralds:

Perilous:

Zeus and Hera
Comprehension Questions

1. Describe Zeus's character.

_____

_____

_____

_____

2. Describe Zeus's powers.

_____

_____

_____

_____

3. Describe how Zeus won Hera's hand in marriage.

_____

_____

_____

_____

4. What did Hera do to try to teach Zeus a lesson? Did it work?

_____

_____

_____

_____

5. What type of goddess was Hera?

_____

_____

_____

_____

Answers to "Zeus and Hera"
Comprehension Questions and Vocabulary Exercises

Discussion Questions

1. Describe Zeus' character.

Zeus was compassionate, yet strong and punishing of those who broke the laws.

2. Describe Zeus's powers.

Zeus was god of the sky and lord of the winds, rain and thunder.

3. Describe how Zeus won Hera's hand in marriage.

Zeus pretended to be a half-frozen cuckoo. She picked up the bird and warmed it against her chest. Zeus changed back into himself. She fell in love with him and they were married.

4. What did Hera do to try and teach Zeus a lesson? Did it work?

Hera thought Zeus was thinking himself too powerful, so she and other gods captured him and tied him up with ropes that contained hundreds of knots. No, it didn't work. It only angered Zeus so much that he dealt out punishments to everyone involved, including Hera.

5. What type of goddess was Hera?

She was a good goddess, wise and caring. She helped mortals overcome many challenges. Her only problem was her temper when angered with Zeus.

Look up each word in the dictionary and write its definition.

Compassionate: showing or feeling compassion or sympathy

Taunted: to provoke or challenge in a mocking or insulting manner

Supplanted: to take the place of another by force

Coronet: a small crown worn by a noble

Heralds: to give notice of, announce

Perilous: full of danger

Fill in the blanks with the correct vocabulary word.

1. He was <u>supplanted</u> by his brother.
2. She wore a <u>coronet</u> on her head.
3. The situation was <u>perilous</u>.
4. The boys <u>taunted</u> the dog.
5. She was announced by the <u>heralds</u>.
6. She felt <u>compassionate</u> toward the hungry kitten, so she fed it.

Write a synonym for vocabulary word.

Compassionate: sympathetic

Taunted: bullied

Supplanted: replaced; overthrown

Coronet: crown

Heralds: announcers

Perilous: dangerous

Zeus and Hera
Creative-Thinking Questions

1. Guess why the gods and goddesses made their home on Mount Olympus.

_____

_____

_____

_____

2. Describe what you think might be a typical day in the life of the gods and goddesses.

_____

_____

_____

_____

3. Analyze Zeus and Hera's relationship.

_____

_____

_____

_____

4. What things might Zeus have done to cause Hera to want to teach him a lesson?

_____

_____

_____

_____

5. Was it wise for the other gods to rebel against Zeus? Give reasons to support your answer.

_____

_____

_____

_____

6. Do you think Thetis expected anything in return for helping Zeus escape? Explain.

_____

_____

_____

_____

7. Suppose you were invited to attend the wedding of Hera and Zeus. What would you give them as a wedding present? Why?

_____

_____

_____

_____

8. Suppose you were Zeus and Hera has left you. What might you do to persuade her to return?

_____

_____

_____

_____

Zeus and Hera
HOW DARE YOU!

Create an adventure Zeus might have had that would have angered Hera.

Zeus and Hera

DIVINE POETRY

Write a poem that Zeus might give to Hera.

Zeus and Hera
IT'S PREDETERMINED

The Fates planned each mortal's life. Pretend to be one of the Fates.
Create a mortal and plan his or her life from birth to death.

Zeus and Hera
A FEAST FIT FOR THE GODS!

The gods and goddesses are celebrating the marriage of Zeus and Hera.
Create a menu for the feast fit for the gods!

Hades, the Underworld and Its Lord

"Hades" has two meanings, the god of the underworld and the place where the dead, both good and bad, would spend eternity. Hades the Underworld played a much bigger part in Greek legends than did the god Hades. The gods enjoyed sending mortals to the underworld for various tasks, such as bringing back a token to prove that they had visited Hades. It took a lot of courage and ingenuity to get in and out of Hades.

When a mortal died, his or her shade, or spirit, was guided to the underworld by Hermes, the messenger god. The way to Hades was very interesting. The dead person was buried with a small coin called an obol placed in his/her mouth. The shade was then led away by Hermes to the threshold of Hades. The shade then had to give the obol to Charon, the ferryman, as payment for Charon rowing him or her across the River Styx. If the dead person was too poor or if the family forgot to place the obol in the shade's mouth, then the shade would be left to wait forever without hope of crossing the Styx. Charon was instructed by Hades, god of the underworld, not to carry any living being across the river. Occasionally, some daring mortal managed to convince him to make an exception, but not often

Once paid, Charon rowed the shade away from the banks of the living and towards the underworld. The three-headed dog, Cerberus, guarded the gates to the underworld. He meant no harm to the shades, but would not let any unauthorized visitors enter through the gate.

Once across the river, the shade had to cross the Plains of Asphodel. This was a misty place filled with shadowy trees with sad, weeping branches. Just past the Plains of Asphodel were the green meadows of Erebus and the pool of Lethe lay. Here the dead would drink from the pool's water and forget their past life in the world above.

Beyond this lay the splendid palace of Hades. After Zeus, Hades and Poseidon overthrew their father, Cronus, they drew lots to see which part of the world they would control. Hades had the worst draw and became lord of the underworld. (In Roman mythology he was also known as Pluto, God of Wealth, because of the great amount of precious metals buried within the earth's depths.) Hades was originally from Olympus, but he spent most of the time in his dark castle in the underworld. His dark personality kept him from being liked by the other gods or mortals. He was not really an evil god; he was stern, unpitying and inexorable, but he was just. Because he ruled the underworld, he was associated with death and feared by men. He wasn't death itself. That was another god, Thanatos.

Hades' weapon was the two-pronged fork. He used this to shatter that which got in his way or wasn't to his liking. His other prized possessions included his helmet, which had been given to him by the Cyclops and which made the wearer invisible, and his dark chariot, which was drawn by four coal-black steeds.

The second path led to the Elysian Fields. The Elysian Fields was a beautiful place. The sun always shone and the sky was blue with white fluffy clouds. Birds sang and the air was filled with beautiful music from the pipes and lyres. Everyone was always happy. Those sent to the Elysian Fields had the choice of returning to earth, but life was so good that few did.

The third path lead to Tartarus, the lowest region and a a place of eternal punishment. The wicked were sent to Tartarus. To enter, one had to pass through a large bronze gate; the gate was always kept locked except when admitting a new shade and was guarded by a giant three-headed monster. A river of fire encircled the walls of Tartarus. Those who inhabited Tartarus were always in pain and their cries of anguish could be heard within the walls.

Some banished to Tartarus were the Titans, or old gods. Cronus was the only one of them who enjoyed the Elysium Fields. The rest were doomed to suffer for eternity.

Another who inhabited Tartarus was Tantalus. He killed the young son of Pelops and served his flesh to the gods to see if they could tell the difference between his meat and the meat of an animal. After the gods found out what he had done, they restored the young man's life. Tantalus's punishment was to stand in a pond under the branch of a fruit tree. He was always hungry and thirsty. Each time he tried to get a piece of fruit, it would shrink back. The same happened with the pond water. The word "tantalize" is derived from his suffering.

Sisyphus, King of Corinth, could also be found in Tartarus. He chained up death when it came for him. For many years no one died on earth. Ares was sent to unchain death so that Hades' Kingdom could be returned to normal. Sisyphus was condemned to push a large boulder to the summit of a hill. Every time he reached the top, the boulder would roll back down and he would have to start over. This went on for eternity. There were many others condemned to Tartarus, each having his or her own story.

Hades was not the only god to live in the underworld; many lesser gods and goddesses lived there as well. Hecate, a daughter of Zeus, had great authority in Hades. She presided over the ceremony of purification for some of the dead who the judges felt could make amends for their past lives.

The three furies—Tisiphone, Alecto and Megaera—also lived in Hades. They had bodies of black dogs, wings of a bat and snakes for hair. Their task was to judge the truth of complaints made by mortals against each other and to deal out punishment to those deemed to be wrong. They especially looked for mortals who broke sacred oaths or who plotted to kill their parents. All those found guilty were punished by the furies. The furies swooped down and killed the wrong-doers with their powerful jaws. They then took their victims to the land of shadows—the underworld.

Hades, the Underworld and Its Lord
Vocabulary Activities

Look up each word in the dictionary and write its definition.

Eternity:

Token:

Ingenuity:

Shade

Inexorable:

Summit

Fill in the blanks with a form of the correct vocabulary word from above.

1. She was _____ in her quest to find the truth.

2. He didn't think he could reach the _____.

3. _____ is really a long time.

4. She used her _____ to solve the problem.

5. She said that the house was haunted and that a _____ roamed the halls.

6. He gave her a ring as a _____ of his affection.

Use the vocabulary words to write a paragraph about the Hades, the Underworld.

Hades, the Underworld and Its Lord
Comprehension Questions

1. Describe the journey of a shade.

_____

_____

_____

_____

2. Describe each of the three places a shade could go in the underworld.

_____

_____

_____

_____

3. Explain how a shade was judged.

_____

_____

_____

_____

4. Tell about some of the inhabitants of Tartarus.

_____

_____

_____

_____

5. Describe the three furies and their job.

_____

_____

_____

_____

Answers to "Hades, the Underworld and Its Lord"
Story Discussion Questions and Vocabulary Exercises

Discussion Questions

1. Describe the journey of a shade.

The body was buried with an obol in his/her mouth. This obol was used to pay Charon, the ferryman to transport him or her across the river to the underworld. The shade was then judged and sent to one of three places: the Plains of Asphodel, the Elysian Fields or Tartarus.

2. Describe each of the three places a shade could go in the underworld.

The Plains of Asphodel was a place of shadows and darkness; these shades led a boring existence with neither pain nor happiness.

The Elysian Fields were a place of happiness, fun, games, music, and lots of food and drink.

Tartarus was a place of torture and everlasting pain.

3. Explain how a shade was judged.

Each shade was judged by three judges. They looked at the shade's life and decided where the shade would reside for eternity.

4. Tell about some who inhabited Tartarus.

The Titans, Tantalus, Sisyphus and many others who were evil or who went against the gods' laws were sent to Tartarus.

5. Describe the three furies and their job.

The furies had bodies of black dogs, a bat's wings and snakes for hair. Their task was to judge the truth of complaints made by mortals against each other and to deal out punishment to those who were deemed wrong.

Look up each word in the dictionary and write its definition.

Eternity: endless time

Token: symbol, expression of something else

Ingenuity: skill or cleverness in discovering, inventing or planning

Shade: a ghost

Inexorable: not to be persuaded; not to be stopped

Summit: the highest point

Fill in the blanks with the correct vocabulary word.

1. She was <u>inexorable</u> in her quest to find the truth.
2. He didn't think he could reach the <u>summit</u>.
3. <u>Eternity</u> is really a long time.
4. She used her <u>ingenuity</u> to solve the problem.
5. She said that the house was haunted and that a <u>shade</u> roamed the halls.
6. He gave her a ring as a <u>token</u> of his affection.

Hades, the Underworld and Its Lord
Creative-Thinking Questions

1. How do you suppose a mortal convinced Charon to row him/her across the Styx?

_____

_____

_____

_____

2. Plan a way to trick Cerberus into allowing you to enter Hades.

_____

_____

_____

_____

3. What might you have done to remind your family to place the obol in your mouth before you were buried so you could pay Charon?

_____

_____

_____

_____

4. What what would you do to achieve a claim to fame so you wouldn't have to spend eternity on the Plains of Asphodel?

_____

_____

_____

_____

5. Why, do you think, were the dead made to drink from the pool of Lethe? What impact might it have had on the underworld if the dead had not drunk from the pool of Lethe?

_____

_____

_____

_____

6. Guess why Hades didn't allow shades to enter his palace.

_____

_____

_____

_____

7. Judge the fact that the shades were judged by three judges. Why not just one?

_____

_____

_____

_____

8. What does the Elysian Fields remind you of? Why?

_____

_____

_____

_____

9. How do you think the gods might have found out about Tantalus's trick?

_____

_____

_____

_____

Hades, the Underworld and Its Lord
WHAT'S IT LIKE?

Draw a picture or a map of the underworld.

Hades, the Underworld and Its Lord
MY HERO

Make up a hero and write a myth about his or her trip to Hades.

Hades, the Underworld and Its Lord
YOU'VE MADE A MISTAKE!

Suppose the judges sent you to the Plains of Asphodel by mistake. How might you convince them of their mistake? Provides examples of your worth.

Hades, the Underworld and Its Lord
BANISHED

Write a story about someone who was banished to Tartarus.

Poseidon, God of the Sea

Poseidon was a son of Cronus. When the three brothers—Zeus, Hades and Poseidon—drew lots as to who would control each part of the world, Poseidon drew the sea and became known as the god of the seas. He was also known as the god of earthquakes and horses. In fact, according to some myths, Poseidon created the horse by striking his trident against a rock. His symbols included the dolphin and his trident, a three-pronged fishing spear.

Poseidon lived in his palace, which was on the floor of the ocean. The palace was <u>adorned</u> with white <u>turrets</u> and arched doorways encrusted with coral and shells. He drove a chariot pulled by two beautiful white horses.

Poseidon was a very <u>ambitious</u> god. He had many disputes with the other deities. He wanted control of not only the seas, but of land as well. The beautiful city in the region later known as Attica especially appealed to him.

The goddess Athene, however, also desired that city. She believed that she should be its patron goddess and that the city should be named for her. Neither Poseidon nor Athene would agree to <u>relinquish</u> claim to the city. In order to settle the conflict, Zeus told each of them to create something useful for the city. Whoever was chosen would be the one to name and protect the city.

Poseidon drove his trident into the Acropolis, causing a spring of water to gush out. When it was her turn, Athene gave the inhabitants the gift of an olive tree. In one version of the myth, a <u>tribunal</u> of gods and goddesses was given the task of deciding which gift was more beneficial. The goddesses all voted for Athene; the gods—with the exception of Zeus, who <u>abstained</u>—voted for Poseidon. Because there was one more goddess than god, Athene won the dispute. The city would be called Athens.

In other versions of the myth the Athenians voted and not the tribunal of gods. They chose the olive tree because it would give them food, oil and wood. The seawater, they said, was not very useful. In still other versions Poseidon gave the people of Athens the gift of a horse.

In any case, Poseidon was very angered by his loss. He called upon the seas to flood the entire region of Attica. In order to appease him, the Athenians continued to worship Poseidon as well as Athene.

Poseidon also had a dispute with Hera, wife of Zeus and queen of the gods. This dispute was over the patronage of Argos. No matter how hard Zeus tried to convince Poseidon to see reason, he would not back down. Zeus decided to ask three river gods—Inachus, Cephissus and Asterion—to decide the matter. They decided in favor of Hera.

Once again Poseidon felt that he had been wronged. He thought the river gods were against him and decided to punish them. Poseidon caused the rivers of the judges to dry up, turning them into dry, crusty roads. The river nymphs and gods stood on the withered banks looking at what once had been their homes. When the rains of winter came, the rivers ran, only to dry up again in the summer.

Poseidon was very moody, and his temper often resulted in violence. In a good mood, he created new lands and calmed the seas. In a bad mood, he caused floods, earthquakes, shipwrecks and drownings. Sailors and warriors prayed to him before heading out to sea. They even drowned their horses as sacrifices to this mighty god of the sea, second only to Zeus in importance in the pantheon of the ancient Greeks.

Poseidon, God of the Sea
Vocabulary Activities

Look up each word in the dictionary and write its definition.

Adorned:

Turrets:

Ambitious:

Relinquish:

Tribunal:

Abstained:

Fill in the blanks with a form of the correct vocabulary word from above.

1. The _____ ruled in favor of the man.

2. Her robe was _____ with gems.

3. He was very _____ to become rich.

4. The _____, which extended above the building, were made of concrete.

5. Mr. Smith liked both candidates equally, so he _____ from the vote.

6. The champion did not want to _____ the title.

Use the vocabulary words to write a paragraph about Poseidon's ocean kingdom.

_____

_____

_____

_____

_____

_____

_____

_____

Poseidon, God of the Sea
Story Discussion Questions

1. Describe Poseidon's personality.

_____

_____

_____

_____

2. What were Poseidon's symbols?

_____

_____

_____

_____

3. Describe Poseidon's underwater castle.

_____

_____

_____

_____

4. Tell about Poseidon's conflict with Athene.

_____

_____

_____

_____

5. What finally satisfied Poseidon?

_____

_____

_____

_____

Answers to "Poseidon, God of the Sea"
Comprehension Questions and Vocabulary Exercises

Discussion Questions

1. Describe Poseidon's personality.

He was ambitious and power hungry. He had a violent temper when angered or didn't get his way.

2. What were Poseidon's symbols?

His symbols were the dolphin and his trident, a three-pronged fish spear. He was also associated with horses.

3. Describe Poseidon's underwater castle.

His castle was adorned with white turrets and arched doorways encrusted with coral and shells.

4. Tell about Poseidon's conflict with Athene.

Poseidon wanted to control Athene's city, Attica. He drove his trident into the Acropolis and caused a spring to gush out. She planted an olive tree beside the stream. She refused to give up control of her city so Poseidon flooded and destroyed Attica.

5. What finally satisfied Poseidon?

He made the rivers dry up during the summer.

Look up each word in the dictionary and write its definition

Adorned: decorated with ornaments

Turrets: small towers often at an angle of a larger structure and merely ornamental

Ambitious: eager desire for success or power

Relinquish: to give up

Tribunal: a court of justice

Abstained: refrained from something by choice

Fill in the blanks with the correct vocabulary word.

1. The <u>tribunal</u> ruled in favor of the man.
2. Her robe was <u>adorned</u> with gems.
3. He was very <u>ambitious</u> to become rich.
4. The <u>turrets,</u> which extended above the building, were made of concrete.
5. Mr. Smith liked both candidates equally, so he <u>abstained</u> from the vote.
6. The champion did not want to <u>relinquish</u> the title.

Poseidon, God of the Sea
Creative-Thinking Questions

1. Knowing the kind of ruler Poseidon was, do you think he would have been a good ruler for mankind? Why or why not?

_____

_____

_____

_____

2. What things might have angered Poseidon enough to make him sink ships and flood the land?

_____

_____

_____

_____

3. Pretend you were sent to Poseidon by Zeus to calm him down. What might you say to him?

_____

_____

_____

_____

4. Guess why Zeus would not allow Athene and Poseidon to fight.

_____

_____

_____

_____

5. Why do you think Athene chose the olive tree to plant beside Poseidon's stream rather than some other type of tree?

_____

_____

_____

_____

6. Suppose Poseidon decided to overthrow Zeus. What would be the outcome?

_____

_____

_____

_____

7. What might have happened had Zeus not sided with Hera?

_____

_____

_____

_____

8. Was Poseidon happy with the river gods' judgment? Why or why not?

_____

_____

_____

_____

Poseidon, God of the Sea
A NEW LAND

Create a new land that Poseidon might have created.
Give details such as appearance, inhabitants, and name.

Poseidon, God of the Sea
HOME, SWEET HOME

Design a palace for Poseidon in his ocean kingdom.
Write a descriptive paragraph about it.

Poseidon, God of the Sea
CREATE A POEM

Write a poem about Poseidon and Athene's conflict.

Poseidon, God of the Sea
WRITE A LETTER

As one of the river gods, write a letter to
Poseidon explaining why you chose the olive tree over his gift.

Prometheus and Pandora

Like other cultures, the ancient Greeks had a myth to explain the creation of man. According to most versions, Zeus gave the job to Prometheus, a Titan who had sided with the Olympian gods when they fought the other Titans. The myth tells us that Prometheus molded the figure of man out of clay in the likeness of the gods.

Epimetheus, his brother, was given the job of bestowing a gift upon each creature of the earth in order to help the creature survive. He gave wings to the birds; claws to the tiger; and a shell to the turtle. When Prometheus told him that he wanted to give the most special gift of all to man, Epimetheus told him that he had already given away all the good gifts.

Prometheus thought about the way men lived (according to some versions of the myth, woman had not yet been created). They kept warm by wrapping themselves in fur. They ate what they could using simple weapons. They grew a few crops. They had neither bowls nor jars in which to store their food because they did not know how to make them.

Prometheus was sympathetic to man and wanted to help him grow more civilized so they could live better lives. He asked Zeus if he could give man the gift of fire—something that until that time had been reserved for the gods. Zeus refused. He was afraid that fire would make man too powerful. He thought that with this power man would want to overthrow the gods.

Prometheus knew he would not be able to get Zeus to change his mind, but he decided to give fire to man anyway. He hid a piece of lit charcoal in the hollow stalk of <u>fennel</u> and gave it to man. He taught man how to use the fire to cook his meat. He showed him how to make pots, vases, bricks for home building and <u>ornaments</u> to decorate his body. Man then learned how to mold metal into swords and spears.

Zeus saw what was happening and was very angry. He was determined to punish Prometheus and Epimetheus. First, however, he would punish man for accepting the godly gift.

Zeus ordered his son Hephaestus to make a girl from clay. Athene gave her the breath of life. She also taught her womanly skills, such as sewing and cooking. Hermes gave her <u>guile</u>, <u>deception</u> and charm. Aphrodite showed her how to make a man love her. The other goddesses dressed her in beautiful clothing. Finally, she was brought to Zeus. Zeus gave the girl, whom he named Pandora, a beautiful chest of copper. He told her that she was never to open it. Pandora thought the chest was full of precious gems and thanked Zeus for his gift.

As part of his plan to punish both the brothers and man, Zeus also gave Pandora to Epimetheus; Epimetheus would take Pandora as his wife. Epimetheus was not as smart as his brother. Although Prometheus warned his brother never to accept a gift from Zeus, Epimetheus did not heed his advice. He was honored that Zeus would choose him to wed Pandora..

At first the couple were very happy. Pandora forgot about the chest. As time passed, however, she began to wonder about it. She asked Epimetheus to give her the key so she could open it, but he refused. Every day Pandora searched for the key. Finally, she found it. While Epimetheus was asleep, she put the key in the lock and lifted the lid. A rushing sound could be heard. Out of the chest flew all evils man deals with today. Hardship, poverty, old age, sickness, jealousy, <u>vice</u>, passion and distrust flew from the chest. Pandora tried to close the lid, but it was too late. She peeked into the chest and one thing remained: hope. She shut the lid, trapping hope in the chest. Because she saved hope, mankind might survive his new world. If hope still exists, anything is possible.

Man had been punished, but Prometheus, who was responsible for giving man the gift of fire, still had to be dealt with. Zeus sent Prometheus to a far away place and had him chained to a rock. Each day an eagle would fly to Prometheus, peck out his liver and eat it. By morning Prometheus would grow a new one and the torture would begin again. Many years Prometheus endured this punishment before he was finally set free.

Zeus's revenge was complete. More importantly, he knew that with all these hardships and challenges, man could never reach his throne. Zeus was now content.

Prometheus and Pandora
Vocabulary Activities

Look up each word in the dictionary and write its definition.

Fennel:

Guile:

Ornament:

Deception:

Vice:

Fill in the blanks with a form of the correct vocabulary word from above.

1. She had a(n) _____ on the front of her dress.

2. His clever _____ tricked her into believing him.

3. The man had a _____ that destroyed his life.

4. The long stem of the _____ had many uses.

5. _____ is not a good trait for a person to have.

Match to vocabulary word to its synonym.

_____ 1. Fennel	A. Shrewdness
_____ 2. Guile	B. Wickedness
_____ 3. Deception	C. Vegetable
_____ 4. Ornament	D. Trick
_____ 5. Vice	E. Decoration

Prometheus and Pandora
Comprehension Questions

1. How does this myth about the creation of man differ from the Judeo-Christian explanation?

_____

_____

_____

_____

2. Why did Prometheus think man needed fire? How did the gift change his life?

_____

_____

_____

_____

3. How did Prometheus's betrayal of Zeus affect Zeus and why?

_____

_____

_____

_____

4. How did Pandora carry out Zeus's revenge?

_____

_____

_____

_____

5. Describe Prometheus's punishment.

_____

_____

_____

_____

Answers to "Prometheus and Pandora"
Comprehension Questions and Vocabulary Exercises

Discussion Questions

1. How does this myth about the creation of man differ from the Judeo-Christian explanation?

According to Greek myths, man was created by Prometheus molding clay in his image and Zeus breathing life into man. Judeo-Christian beliefs state that God created man in his image.

2. Why did Prometheus think man needed fire? How did the gift change his life?

The first man was very primitive. He ate his meat raw, used wooden weapons and grew a few crops. He kept warm by wrapping himself in furs. By Prometheus giving man fire, man was able to improve his life. He learned how to cook his food, make better weapons and sturdier homes through bricks.

3. How did Prometheus's betrayal of Zeus affect Zeus and why?

Zeus was afraid that man would gain power and decide to overthrow him. It made Zeus angry.

3. Describe Prometheus's punishment.

Prometheus was chained to a mountain. An eagle pecked away at his liver. When the liver was devoured, it grew back to be devoured again.

5. How did Pandora carry out Zeus's revenge?

Zeus planned for her to open the chest and let all types of evils out on man. He knew that her curiosity would keep her from obeying him.

Look up each word in the dictionary and write its definition.

Fennel: a garden plant related to the carrot and grown for its aromatic foliage and seeds

Guile: skillful deceit; cunning

Ornament: something that adds beauty

Deception: misrepresentation; misleading falsehood

Vice: evil conduct or habits; a moral fault

Fill in the correct word for each sentence.

1. She had an ornament on the front of her dress.
2. His deception tricked her into believing him.
3. The man had a vice that destroyed his life.
4. The long stem of the fennel had many uses.
5. Guile is not a good trait for a person to possess.

Match the vocabulary word to its synonym.

_C_	1. Fennel	A. Shrewdness
_A_	2. Guile	B. Wickedness
_D_	3. Deception	C. Vegetable
_E_	4. Ornament	D. Trick
_B_	5. Vice	E. Decoration

Prometheus and Pandora
Creative-Thinking Questions

1. What are some reasons you might have given Zeus to convince him that it would be to his advantage for man to become civilized?

_____

_____

_____

_____

2. Prometheus used fennel to sneak fire off Mount Olympus for man. What other way might Prometheus have gotten fire to man?

_____

_____

_____

_____

3. How might Prometheus have tricked Zeus into thinking he was not the one who gave man the gift of fire?

_____

_____

_____

_____

4. How might man's life have been different had he not been given fire?

_____

_____

_____

_____

5. What other plan might Zeus have used to get revenge on man?

_____

_____

_____

_____

6. Do you think Zeus enjoyed his revenge. Why or why not?

_____

_____

_____

_____

7. What might Epimetheus have done to keep Pandora from opening the chest?

_____

_____

_____

_____

8. When do you think Pandora realized her mistake? Give reasons for your opinion.

_____

_____

_____

_____

Prometheus and Pandora
BREAKING NEWS!

Write a radio show about the myth of Pandora's Box.
Be sure to include your opinion about the incident in your report.

Prometheus and Pandora
A BETTER WORLD!

Write about a world without all the evils that Pandora let out of the chest.

Prometheus and Pandora
A WORLD WITHOUT...

If you could keep one of the evils in the box from entering our world, which would you choose? Why? How might that have made a difference?

Prometheus and Pandora
I'M SORRY!

Pretend that you are Zeus and that you feel remorseful about the Pandora incident. How could you fix it so that mankind would not suffer so?

Aphrodite, Goddess of Love and Beauty, and Hephaestus, God of Fire

Mount Olympus was celebrating the coming of a new child for Zeus and Hera. Zeus predicted it would be a son and named him Hephaestus. Hephaestus would become the god of fire. He later developed into the god of those industries that depended upon fire, such as pottery and metallurgy.

When Hephaestus was born, however, he was deformed and ugly. He was kept from Hera as long as possible. When Hera finally saw her son, she flew into a rage and denied that he was hers. Although some versions say that Zeus threw him from Olympus later on, according to one popular version of the myth, Hera seized Hephaestus and threw him from Olympus. Luckily, he fell into the arms of two <u>Nereids</u>, Thetis and Eurynome. They raised him in their underworld home as their own son. He grew up happy.

Hephaestus, often called the smith god, developed a talent for iron work. He made beautiful jewelry and other works of art. Thetis and Eurynome often wore beautiful bracelets and necklaces that Hephaestus made for them.

One day Thetis received an invitation to attend a feast on Olympus. She dressed in her finest clothing and chose one of the pendants that Hephaestus had made for her to wear. As Thetis gazed upon the blue and pearl <u>pendant</u>, she knew everyone would envy her.

Upon her arrival, Hera admired the beautiful pendant. She asked Thetis where she had gotten it. Thetis was reluctant to tell her, but finally she revealed that it was given to her by Hephaestus, the son that Hera had cast to earth.

Hera sent a messenger to Hephaestus to come and visit her at Olympus. He was not interested in seeing Hera. He knew she was his mother and had not wanted him. Hephaestus did send Hera a beautiful gold chair, however, convincing her that it was a peace offering. Bragging to everyone, she seated herself on the thrown. When she tried to get out of the chair, she could not move. She stuck tight to her golden thrown.

Angrily, she called Zeus to come and help her, but only Hephaestus could set her free. Zeus sent messengers to Hephaestus to release her, but he refused. Finally, Dionysus was sent to give him wine. Once Hephaestus was sufficiently <u>fuddled</u>, Dionysus brought him to Olympus.

The gods of Olympus pleaded with him to set her free. They even gave him a place in Olympus. Still he would not agree to their demands. It wasn't until Zeus offered him the beautiful Aphrodite, the goddess of love, as his wife that he agreed to set Hera free.

The gods of Olympus created a large workshop with a forge for him. He was given everything he needed to make special objects for the gods. Hephaestus made them beautiful palaces, special weapons and equipment, furniture and other magnificent objects for them. According to some, it was he who made the magic <u>girdle</u> worn by Aphrodite. This girdle gave her the power to make any man fall in love with her. He even made himself a pair of gold braces for his legs.

Hephaestus was lame and needed the braces to walk. In some versions of the myth Hephaestus became lame when Hera threw him out of Olympus upon seeing him at birth. In other versions, Zeus threw him from Olympus because Hephaestus sided with Hera in an argument.

Aphrodite, Hephaestus's bride, was known as the most beautiful of all women. Her beginning was a very strange story. After Cronus killed his father, Uranus, his body was <u>dismembered</u> and thrown into the sea. A column of foam boiled out of the water and from this foam came Aphrodite.

Zeus heard of her strange birth and had her brought to Olympus. The gods were in <u>awe</u> of her great beauty. Many argued over her. Poseidon thought she should be his because she came from the sea. Hermes tried to fly her around the world, but she wasn't interested in him. Even Apollo tried to make her his by singing her beautiful love songs.

Aphrodite could have had any man she wanted, but she didn't have the opportunity to choose. Zeus did not like the fact that the gods were fighting over her. He decided that it would be best if she married Hephaestus.

When Aphrodite was told that she would marry Hephaestus, she was quite disappointed. He was not at all handsome. His legs were encased in gold braces, and his head was as big as a giant's. However, Aphrodite knew that everyone was watching her to see how she would react. She just smiled and embraced him.

Once Aphrodite had a chance to think about the marriage, she decided that it wasn't such a bad idea. She knew that Hephaestus would not try to rule her, so she would have the freedom to do as she pleased, which she did!

Aphrodite and Hephaestus
Vocabulary Activities

Look up each word in the dictionary and write its definition.

Nereids:

Pendant:

Fuddled:

Girdle:

Dismembered:

Awe:

Fill in the blanks with a form of the correct vocabulary word from above.

1. She wore a beautiful _____ around her neck.

2. The angry child _____ the doll.

3. He became _____ after smelling the gas.

4. The _____ lived in the sea.

5. The _____ was too small for anyone else to wear around the waist.

6. The boys were in _____ of the star football player.

Make up a new god or goddess and write about him or her using the vocabulary words.

Aphrodite and Hephaestus
Comprehension Questions

1. How did Hera react to the birth of her son and why?

_____

_____

_____

_____

2. Describe Hephaestus's talent.

_____

_____

_____

_____

3. Tell about Hephaestus's gift to his mother.

_____

_____

_____

_____

4. Tell about Aphrodite's birth.

_____

_____

_____

_____

5. How did Aphrodite react to having to marry Hephaestus and why?

_____

_____

_____

_____

Answers to "Aphrodite and Hephaestus"
Comprehension Questions and Vocabulary Exercises

Discussion Questions

1. How did Hera react to the birth of her son and why?

She was very upset that her baby was disfigured. She denied that he was hers and threw him off Olympus.

2. Describe Hephaestus's talent.

He was very good at working with iron.

3. Tell about Hephaestus' gift to his mother.

Hephaestus made his mother a beautiful golden thrown. She sat down in it and became trapped. She could not get out. Hephaestus was finally persuaded to set her free.

4. Tell about Aphrodite's birth.

She arose from the sea where Uranus's dismembered body had been thrown.

5. How did Aphrodite react to having to marry Hephaestus and why?

Aphrodite was very disappointed at having to marry Hephaestus because she felt he was below her. She could have had any god or mortal that she wanted, but was ordered to marry Hephaestus. She did like the idea that he would not try and control her so she could have her freedom.

Look up each word's definition in the dictionary.

Nereids: sea nymphs who are the daughters of Nereus, the sea god

Pendant: an ornament that hangs down

Fuddled: muddled, confused

Dismembered: to cut off or separate the limbs or parts

Awe: feeling of mixed fear, respect and wonder

Girdle: a belt or sash encircling the waist

Fill in the blanks with the correct vocabulary word.

1. She wore a beautiful <u>pendant</u> around her neck.
2. The angry child <u>dismembered</u> the doll.
3. He became <u>fuddled</u> after smelling the gas.
4. The <u>Nereids</u> lived in the sea.
5. The <u>girdle</u> was too small for anyone else to wear around the waist.
6. The boys were in <u>awe</u> of the star football player.

Aphrodite and Hephaestus
Creative-Thinking Questions

1. What might have happened to Hephaestus had the Nereids not caught him and raised him as their own?

_____

_____

_____

_____

2. Describe Hephaestus's feelings towards his mother because of what she did to him. Do you think he forgave her? Why or why not?

_____

_____

_____

_____

3. Suppose you were walking along and a baby fell into your arms. What would you do?

_____

_____

_____

_____

4. Hephaestus had a special talent for working with iron. Do you have a special talent or something you really enjoy doing? If so, tell about it.

_____

_____

_____

_____

5. What else might Hephaestus have done in order to punish his mother besides trapping her on the golden throne?

_____

_____

_____

_____

6. Do you think Aphrodite took advantage of men? Explain.

_____

_____

_____

_____

7. Was it right for Zeus to command Aphrodite to marry Hephaestus? Why or why not?

_____

_____

_____

_____

8. How might you teach Aphrodite a lesson and humble her?

_____

_____

_____

_____

Aphrodite and Hephaestus
BIRTH OF A GODDESS

Write an original story describing different events
explaining the birth of Aphrodite.

Aphrodite and Hephaestus
YOU'RE UNDER MY SPELL

Suppose you are Hephaestus.
Devise a way to make Aphrodite fall in love with you and stay true to you.

Aphrodite and Hephaestus
BRAVO!

Write about someone who has a special talent that you admire.

Aphrodite and Hephaestus
WHAT A PAIR!

Write a paragraph about Hephaestus and Aphrodite's relationship.

Artemis, Goddess of the Hunt, and Apollo, God of Truth and Music

According to Greek myths, the gods did not believe that—for them at least—marriage had to be a life-long commitment. Even though Hestia, goddess of the <u>hearth</u> and symbol of the home, was important, the gods did not necessarily abide by the <u>consecrated</u> marriage.

Zeus was the worst example of a faithful husband. He was always pursuing beautiful girls. Leto, daughter of the Titans was one of his conquests. She lived in Olympus. When Hera heard that Leto was going to have Zeus's child, she <u>banished</u> her to earth and sent a python to pursue her wherever she went. Leto could not get any rest.

Nine months later she gave birth to Artemis and Apollo. Both children were beautiful. When they were three, Zeus came and visited them. He decided that they should be brought to Olympus.

When the twins were older, Zeus gave each a gift. To Apollo he gave a golden chariot, drawn by white horses. He also gave him a golden bow and a <u>quiver</u> of golden arrows. Apollo became the god of truth, music and healing.

Artemis was given a choice. She asked for a silver chariot, a bow with arrows, a hunting tunic, a pack of fierce hounds, and twenty wood nymphs and twenty water nymphs to be her hand-maidens and companions.

Artemis enjoyed running through the woods and hunting. After receiving her gifts, she sent her hounds out to find her two fine <u>hinds</u>, warning the hounds not to harm them. When they brought the hinds back, she harnessed them to her chariot and dashed into the hills with her nymphs and hounds running before her.

She was anxious to try out her new bow. That night she found a good target, a tall pine tree. She drew back her arrow and let it fly, splitting the tree in half. She then searched for another target. At last she came to an city that was inhabited by wicked people. Artemis drew back her magic arrow and let it fly into the center of the town. It scattered into thousands of shining deadly pieces, killing everyone in the city.

From that time on, Artemis became known as the goddess of the chase, or the huntress of the gods. She was also known as the mistress of animals and the protectress of children. Artemis was associated with the moon,too, because she enjoyed hunting by the light of the moon.

Artemis wasn't interested in men and vowed never to marry. She made her nymphs take the same vow. Not all obeyed, however. One nymph, Callisto, was pursued by Zeus and gave in to his attention.

When Artemis found out, she became very angry. She turned her into a bear, planning to hunt her down and kill her. Zeus learned of her plan and snatched Callisto before Artemis could kill her. He placed the bear in the sky where she can still be seen today.

Apollo, too, was learning to use his bow and arrows. He remembered how the python would not let his mother rest during her pregnancy. He found the python and aimed his golden bow, letting an arrow fly. The arrow only wounded the python. It fled to the Shrine of Delphi and hid. Apollo hunted it down and killed it.

The Shrine of Delphi was a sacred place. The python's death at the Shrine enraged the gods. Apollo claimed Delphi to be his own; however. He ordered games to be played there each year, celebrating his victory over the python.

Apollo was not only a great hunter, but also a wonderful musician. His music could not be matched by anyone. One day Apollo heard that a satyr named Marsyas had bragged that he could play the flute better than Apollo could play his lyre. Apollo immediately challenged the satyr to a musical battle. The Muses would be the judges.

Marsyas was frightened. He knew he had been foolish to brag about being better than a god, but it was too late. He had no choice but to accept the challenge. First one played, then the other. They were both so good that the Muses could not decide who was better.

Apollo didn't like the fact that his superiority was being questioned, so he issued another test. He challenged Marsyas to turn his flute upside down and play. Apollo would do the same with his lyre. Apollo played first, making beautiful music. Marsyas turned his flute upside down, but the instrument could not be played upside down. Apollo had tricked him and won.

Apollo's punishment of Marsyas was severe. He was flayed alive and his skin was nailed to a pine tree. This was a lesson for all who thought to challenge the gods!

Artemis and Apollo
Vocabulary Activities

Look up each word in the dictionary and write its definition.

Consecrated:

Hearth:

Banished:

Quiver:

Hinds:

Fill in the blanks with a form of the correct vocabulary word from above.

1. The fire in the _____ was kept burning at all times.

2. The _____ held his magical arrows.

3. The _____ grounds were only for the gods

4. The beautiful red _____ ran gracefully through the woods.

5. He was _____ from the land for his actions against the gods.

Use each vocabulary word in a sentence about Greek Mythology.

Artemis and Apollo
Comprehension Questions

1. Describe what led up to the birth of Artemis and Apollo.

_____

_____

_____

_____

2. Describe Artemis. Include her gifts, talents and goddess jobs.

_____

_____

_____

_____

3. Describe Apollo. Include his gifts, talents and goddess jobs.

_____

_____

_____

_____

4. How did Artemis deal with the evil city?

_____

_____

_____

_____

5. Tell about Apollo's challenge to Marsyas.

_____

_____

_____

_____

Answers to "Artemis and Apollo"
Comprehension Questions and Vocabulary Exercises

Discussion Questions

1. Describe what led up to the birth of Artemis and Apollo.

Zeus fathered the children with Leto. This made Hera angry, so she sent a python to follow Leto until she gave birth to Zeus's twins.

2. Describe Artemis. Include her gifts, talents and goddess jobs.

Artemis asked Zeus for a silver chariot, a bow, arrows, a hunting tunic, a pack of fierce hounds, and wood and water nymphs to be her handmaidens. Her talent was being a great huntress. She was known as the goddess of the chase, mistress of animals, and protectress of children. She was also associated with the moon.

3. Describe Apollo. Include his gifts, talents and job as a god.

Apollo was given a golden chariot drawn by white horses and a golden bow and quiver of golden arrows. He was a very talented musician. He could play the lyre. He was the god of truth, music and healing.

4. How did Artemis deal with the evil city?

She took aim and sent an arrow flying into the middle of the city. It splintered into many pieces killing everyone in the city.

5. Tell about Apollo's challenge to Marsyas.

Marsyas bragged that he could play his flute better than Apollo could play his lyre. Apollo heard of this and challenged Marsyas to a musical play-off. He asked the Muses to judge the competition. The Muses could not make up their minds, so Apollo issued another challenge: to play the instruments upside down. The flute could not be played upside down. Apollo had tricked Marsyas and won the challenge.

Look up each of the vocabulary words in the dictionary and write their definitions.

Consecrated: to set apart for the service of god

Hearth: the area in front of the fireplace

Banished: to force to leave a country

Quiver: a case for carrying arrows

Hinds: a female deer

Hubris:

Fill in the blank with the correct vocabulary word.

1. The fire in the <u>hearth</u> was kept burning at all times.
2. The <u>quiver </u>held his magical arrows.
3. The <u>consecrated</u> grounds were only for the gods
4. The beautiful red <u>hinds</u> ran gracefully through the woods.
5. He was <u>banished</u> from the land for his actions against the gods.

Artemis and Apollo
Creative-Thinking Questions

1. Describe the meaning of the hearth as a symbol of the home.

_____

_____

_____

_____

2. Artemis asked for more than Apollo. Do you think this was this a sign of her personality?

_____

_____

_____

_____

3. If you were a child of Zeus, what would you ask for?

_____

_____

_____

_____

4. Guess why Hera chose a phython to chase Leto rather than another creature.

_____

_____

_____

_____

5. Was it fair of Artemis to insist that her nymphs never marry just because she didn't want to marry?

_____

_____

_____

_____

6. Who were the Muses?

_____

_____

_____

_____

7. What might have happened had the Muses chosen Marsyas as the winner?

_____

_____

_____

_____

8. Was it right for Apollo to trick Marsyas as he did? Give reasons for your opinion.

_____

_____

_____

_____

9. Do you think Apollo would have chosen a less severe punishment if the Muses had chosen him immediately instead of being undecided? Give reasons for your opinion.

_____

_____

_____

_____

Artemis and Apollo
THAT'LL TEACH HIM!

Change the ending of the story about Apollo and Marsyas so that Apollo inflicts a more civilized punishment upon Marsyas that would still teach him a lesson.

Artemis and Apollo
I WARNED YOU!

Write a letter to Marsyas from Athene, who was the original owner of his flute.

Artemis and Apollo
A DIFFERENT LIFE

How would the twins' life have been different if they had stayed on earth?

Artemis and Apollo
I CHALLENGE YOU!

Suppose you were going to challenge a god or goddess? How might you do it and still remain alive whether you win or lose?

Phæthon and the Chariot of the Sun

Helios, the sun god, drove his chariot across the sky each day. His chariot was made of gold and was drawn by four fiery mares. Upon his head he wore a golden jeweled helmet to protect him from the intense heat. He left from the east and headed west causing the rising and setting of the sun. People could not look at him without shading their eyes. Every night he went home and rested so he could perform his duties the next morning.

Phæthon was Helios's son. Every day he watched his father ride across the sky. But he could only see him from a distance, for he was raised in a land far from his father. Phæthon often bragged to his friends that Helios was his father. However, they began to make fun of him because they did not believe that the sun god was really his father. They thought Phæthon's father had left him and his mother.

Following the advice of his mother, the sea nymph Clymene, Phæthon went to the land where the sun rises to look for Helios. He found him and asked for proof that he was indeed his father.

Helios wanted to <u>acknowledge</u> his son. He told him that as proof he would grant him *any* one request. Helios had no idea that his son would request anything as foolish as driving the sun-chariot across the sky! He begged Phæthon to choose a different request, but his son would not change his mind. Helios finally agreed. He gave him a special ointment to protect him from the heat and warned him to stay in the middle zone so that all areas of the land would receive the proper amount of heat.

Morning found Phæthon in the golden chariot, grasping the reigns and cracking the whip over the horses' heads. Off they flew. The horses seemed <u>docile</u>. This gave Phæthon the confidence he needed to soar up into the sky. As Phæthon held the reins he remembered his father's warning: "You must drive neither too high nor too low. Follow the broad path that has been traveled since the beginning of time and always keep your hands firmly on the reins."

As Phæthon made his way towards the heavens, he brought with him the first glimpse of light. At first the horses continued down the same path they had traveled for eternity, but they soon sensed a difference on their reins. Their eyes lit with a sense of freedom.

Phæthon looked down and saw the tiny houses where his friends lived. He knew that from this far distance, they could not see that it was he and not his father driving the chariot. He cracked the whip above the horses' heads and guided them downward. The horses went too close to the houses, setting them on fire. His friends dove for cover as the fiery chariot approached.

The horses now knew they were in control. They <u>skimmed</u> along the earth's surface bringing destruction with them. Trees and grass caught fire. The crops were destroyed. Cities were left in ashes. As Phæthon flew over Egypt, he turned it into a barren desert except for a thin line, which was the Nile.

Phæthon realized he had to take the chariot higher. He pushed the horses upward, causing the earth to freeze and seas to turn into great blocks of ice. Devastation followed Phæthon and the fiery chariot.

Phæthon cried to his father for help. Unfortunately, Helios could do nothing. Zeus was watching from above and took control. He threw a thunderbolt at the boy, causing him to fall from the chariot and plunge to his death.

Helios began looking for his runaway chariot and horses, finding them high in the mountains. <u>Parched</u> land could be seen from miles. Helios threw his <u>cloak</u> over the horses' heads, calming them down. He flew slowly back home. Darkness fell across the land as Helios <u>mourned</u> the death of his foolish son.

Phæthon and the Chariot of the Sun
Vocabulary Activities

Look up each word in the dictionary and write its definition.

Docile:

Skimmed:

Cloak:

Parched:

Mourned:

Fill in the blanks with a form of the correct vocabulary word from above.

1. The oar _____ the surface of the water, hardly touching it.

2. The desert was _____ because of the heat and lack of rain.

3. Her gentle animals were very _____ when petted.

4. The boy _____ the death of his dog.

5. His _____ protected him from the cold wind.

Write a synonym for each word.

Docile:

Skimmed:

Cloak:

Parched:

Mourned:

Phæthon and the Chariot of the Sun
Comprehension Questions

1. Describe Helios and his responsibilities.

_____

_____

_____

_____

2. Why was Phæthon so upset and what did he do about it?

_____

_____

_____

_____

3. What problems did Phæthon have when driving his father's chariot?

_____

_____

_____

_____

4. Why did Zeus become involved? What was his solution to the problem?

_____

_____

_____

_____

5. Describe the devastation left by Phæthon's journey.

_____

_____

_____

_____

Answers to "Phæthon and the Chariot of the Sun" Comprehension Questions and Vocabulary Exercises

Discussion Questions

1. Describe Helios and his responsibilities.

Helios was the sun god. He wore a golden jeweled helmet. He drove his chariot around the earth each day, causing the sun to rise and set.

2. Why was Phæthon so upset and what did he do about it?

Phæthon was upset because his friends did not believe him when he said his father was Helios. He decided to ask his father if he could drive his father's chariot to convince his friends.

3. What problems did Phæthon have when driving his father's chariot?

He was so far away that his friends could not see him drive the chariot. He could not control the horses, so they went wherever they wanted. They destroyed some of the earth because some areas got too much heat and some not enough.

4. Why did Zeus decide to get involved? What was his solution?

Zeus became involved because the land was being destroyed and Helios was unable to help.

5. Describe the devastation left by Phæthon's journey.

Egypt was left as a wasteland, rivers and seas were turned into large blocks of ice and homes were burned.

Look up each word in the dictionary and write its definition.

Docile: easily taught, led or managed

Skimmed: glided or passed quickly and lightly over or along a surface

Cloak: a long loose outer garment

Parched: to wilt with heat

Mourned: felt or showed grief, especially over someone's death

Fill in the blanks with the correct vocabulary word.

1. The oar <u>skimmed</u> the surface of the water, hardly touching it.
2. The <u>desert</u> was parched because of the heat and lack of rain.
3. Her gentle animals were very <u>docile</u> when petted.
4. The boy <u>mourned</u> the death of his dog.
5. His <u>cloak</u> protected him from the cold wind.

Write a synonym for each word.

Docile: calm

Skimmed: glided

Cloak: coat

Parched: dry

Mourned: grieved

Phæthon and the Chariot of the Sun
Creative-Thinking Questions

1. Why, do you think, was Phæthon raised far from his father's palace?

_____

_____

_____

_____

2. Suppose Phæthon had been raised by his father around the horses. Might the outcome have been different? Explain.

_____

_____

_____

_____

3. What other means might Phæthon have used to convince his friends that Helios was his father?

_____

_____

_____

_____

4. Why, do you think, did Helios finally agree to let his son drive the chariot?

_____

_____

_____

_____

5. If you were his mother or father, what might you have done or said to Phæthon to persuade him to change his request?

_____

_____

_____

_____

6. Judge Zeus's decision to throw the thunderbolt. What might you have done differently to save both the land and the boy?

_____

_____

_____

_____

7. Had Phæthon listened to his father, how might the earth be different today?

_____

_____

_____

_____

8. Judge Helios's decision to let his son ride the chariot. Think about why he made that decision and the fact that he mourned his son afterwards. What does this tell you about his character and the kind of god he was?

_____

_____

_____

_____

Phæthon and the Chariot of the Sun
AN EPITAPH

An epitaph is an inscription on a tombstone.
Write an epitaph for Phæthon's tombstone in the form of a poem.

Phæthon and the Chariot of the Sun
WHAT WERE YOU THINKING?

Write a letter to Helios from Clymene, mother of Phæthon.

Phæthon and the Chariot of the Sun
INTERVIEW WITH A GOD

Write an "on-the-scene" report describing Phæthon's adventure in the chariot.

Phæthon and the Chariot of the Sun
A LESSON TO BE LEARNED

Use the myth about Phæthon to teach a lesson to younger children.

Athene, Goddess of Wisdom, and Arachne

Hera was not Zeus's only wife. He had been married to Metis after a long <u>courtship</u>. When Zeus was pursuing Metis, she turned herself into a fish trying to escape him. He just turned himself into a fish and swam after her. She leaped from the water and turned herself into an eagle. Zeus became an eagle and flew after her. It seemed she could not escape him, so she conceded to his will and they were married.

One day Zeus went to the <u>Oracle</u> of Delphi. She told Zeus that he would have a daughter who would bring many gifts. The Oracle went on to warn Zeus that he would also have a son who would overthrow him—as he had done to his father Cronus—and replace him as leader of the gods.

Zeus was not happy with this prophecy. He would not take the risk of having a child with Metis. Zeus summoned her to the garden, turned her into a fly and swallowed her. Now, he thought, Metis would not be a threat to him. What he did not know was that Metis was already carrying his child, the child who one day would be known as the goddess Athene.

Zeus soon developed a severe headache. No remedy seemed to help. Zeus called for Hephaestus and commanded him to get rid of the evil spirit that caused him so much pain. Hephaestus took his hammer and hit Zeus in the head so the spirit could escape. Instead, a beautiful young girl with blue eyes and golden hair popped out of his head. She was dressed in full armor and held a spear. This was Metis' child, his daughter. Zeus could not reject his own daughter, so he acknowledged her as such and named her Athene.

As Athene grew to womanhood it was apparent that she was very wise and gifted. Not only was she the goddess of wisdom, but also of the arts. She was first to spin wool and from it make cloth. She taught man how to make the wheel, the axe, the flute and the trumpet. She showed him how to plow and how to sail ships.

Athene also helped others solve their arguments by using reasonable debate. Although her nature was peaceful, however, her skill in war strategy was tested many times. She always tried for a peaceful solution first. Only after this failed did she resort to violence.

One time Athene did let jealousy rule over her. There was a young girl named Arachne. She was very skilled at weaving She made a huge <u>tapestry</u> that portrayed stories of the gods. The scenes appeared to move across the tapestry. It attracted people from all over the land.

Everyone's compliments filled her full of <u>vanity</u>. She began bragging that she could weave better than the goddess Athene. Athene heard of these boasts and decided to see for herself. She came down from Mount Olympus to look at the tapestry.

As soon as Arachne saw her, she knelt down before her, regretting her boastfulness. Athene asked to see the tapestry. She looked at each stitch, noting how the colors seemed to blend together. Her blue eyes became dark. She realized that Arachne could weave better than she.

Athene was Zeus' daughter. She tried to control her passionate jealousy, which was inherited from her father, but the tapestry was too much. She grabbed the beautiful tapestry and tore it into pieces. There was nothing left of Arachne's art.

Arachne left, walking into the forest. She no longer wished to live and she hanged herself. Athene was sorry for losing control and causing Arachne's death. She decided to change Arachne into a tiny spider so that she could weave for all eternity.

Athene and Arachne
Vocabulary Activities

Look up each word in the dictionary and write its definition.

Courtship:

Oracle:

Summoned:

Remedy:

Tapestry:

Vanity:

Fill in the blank with the correct vocabulary word.

1. The beautiful _____ hung on the wall.

2. He used an old _____ to cure her cold.

3. Their _____ was long, but finally they married.

4. The maid was _____ by her master.

5. Her _____ caused her to constantly look in the mirror.

6. They listened to the _____ about their future.

Write a paragraph using the vocabulary words to tell Arachne's story from her viewpoint.

_____

_____

_____

_____

_____

_____

_____

_____

_____

Athene, Goddess of Wisdom
Comprehension Questions

1. Describe Athene's birth.

_____

_____

_____

_____

2. Tell about Athene's contributions to mankind.

_____

_____

_____

_____

3. Describe Athene's personality.

_____

_____

_____

_____

4. What was special about Arachne? How did this affect Athene?

_____

_____

_____

_____

5. What happened to Arachne's tapestry? What happened to Arachne?

_____

_____

_____

_____

Answers to "Athene, Goddess of Wisdom"
Comprehension Questions and Vocabulary Exercises

Discussion Questions

1. Describe Athene's birth.

Zeus swallowed Athene's mother because he feared that she might bear a son who would some-day overthrow him. Zeus had a terrible headache. Hephaestus used his hammer and hit Zeus on the head. From his head came Athene.

2. Tell about Athene's contributions to mankind.

Athene taught man how to weave; how to make the wheel, axe, flute and trumpet; how to plow; and how to sail ships. She also taught him the art of solving arguments through discussion.

3. Describe Athene's personality.

Athene was peaceful; however, when the need arose, she could resort to violence. She could also show jealousy.

4. What was special about Arachne and how did this talent affect Athene?

Arachne was a great weaver. This made Athene jealous.

5. What happened to Arachne's tapestry? What happened to Arachne?

Athene saw it and realized that Arachne was a better weaver than she, so Athene tore it to pieces. Arachne tried to hang herself, and Athene turned her into a spider.

Look up each word in the dictionary and write its definition.

Courtship: the act of gaining attention for a relationship

Oracle: a person whom through a god speak is believed to speak

Summoned: to call or send for in order to meet

Remedy: a medicine or treatment that cures or relieves

Tapestry: a heavy cloth with pictures woven into it; it is usually used as a wall hanging

Vanity: excessive pride or conceit

Fill in the blank with the correct vocabulary word.

1. The beautiful <u>tapestry</u> hung on the wall.

2. He used an old <u>remedy</u> to cure her cold.

3. Their <u>courtship</u> was long, but finally they married.

4. The maid was <u>summoned</u> by her master.

5. Her <u>vanity</u> caused her to constantly look in the mirror.

6. They listened to the <u>oracle</u> about their future.

Athene, Goddess of Wisdom
Creative-Thinking Questions

1. Compare Zeus in this myth to Cronus in the myth about "The Beginning."

_____

_____

_____

_____

2. Judge Metis's actions when Zeus swallowed her.

_____

_____

_____

_____

3. How might future events have differed if Zeus had not allowed Athene to live?

_____

_____

_____

_____

4. How might Arachne have convinced Athene not to rip up the tapestry?

_____

_____

_____

_____

5. Judge Athene's decision to rip up the tapestry.

_____

_____

_____

_____

6. Judge Athene's choice of a spider when deciding what to do with Arachne. What other creature might have been suitable? Why?

_____

_____

_____

_____

7. Suppose the two women had gotten along. What might they have worked on together?

_____

_____

_____

_____

8. What might Athene have done to stop Arachne from killing herself?

_____

_____

_____

_____

Athene, Goddess of Wisdom
WEAVE A STORY

Design a tapestry that depicts a Greek myth.

Athene, Goddess of Wisdom
CREATE A POEM

Write a poem about the conflict between Athene and Arachne.

Athene, Goddess of Wisdom
AND SO THEY SPIN

Write your own tale about how spiders came to spin webs.

Athene, Goddess of Wisdom
WHAT WOULD WE DO?

Write about how the world would be without the wheel.

Perseus and the Gorgons

Perseus was the son of Zeus and a mortal named Danae. King, Polydectes of Seriphus was in love with Danae. Danae stayed by her side, preventing him from <u>abducting</u> her. Polydectes wanted to get rid of Perseus and tricked Perseus into agreeing to bring him the head of the Gorgon named Medusa. He was certain the mission would lead to his death.

Medusa lived on an <u>arid</u> island with the two other Gorgons, her sisters Stheno and Euryale. The Gorgons were terrible monsters, half-dragon and half-woman. They had scales on their bodies, and their hands were solid <u>brass</u>. Their faces were beautiful, yet terrible. Their hair was made up of hundreds of poisonous snakes, constantly hissing of danger. The worst part about the Gorgons was that whoever looked upon them would be instantly turned into stone.

As the gods and goddesses watched as Perseus began his <u>quest</u>, they smiled upon him, giving him their favors. Hermes and Athene instructed Perseus to find the three Graeae, for they could help him get to the Gorgons, who were their sisters. The Graeae shared one eye and one tooth; they passed each around from one to the other. The gods told Perseus that the sisters would give him the necessary items to complete his task successfully.

With the help of Athene and Hermes, Perseus found the Graeae. He took their eye and their tooth and held the items as <u>ransom</u> until the sisters gave him what he wanted: winged sandals so he could fly and escape; the helmet of Hades, which would make him invisible; a sickle, which had been used by both Cronos and Zeus, to decapitate Medusa; and a bag in which to put the head so he would not have to view it. Athene gave him her shield and told him to use it to reflect the image of Medusa; she said that would prevent him from being turned into stone. (According to another version, the Graeae directed him to the Stygian Nymphs, who told him where to find the Gorgons and gave him the bag, sandals, and helmet. In this version Hermes gave him the sword.)

Perseus placed the winged sandals on his feet and flew to the dreaded island of the Gorgons. He would not look directly at the island, but used Athene's shield to reflect the surroundings. Soon he saw the reflection of the three Gorgons; they were sleeping soundly on the rocks. He swooped down and with one blow of the sickle cut off Medusa's head.

Perseus quickly grabbed the head and wrapped it in his <u>cloak</u>, putting it in the goatskin bag that had been given to him by the Graeae. The snakes of her hair could be heard hissing through the bag. This awoke the other Gorgons. However, Perseus was wearing Pluto's helmet, which made him invisible. He escaped without the other two even knowing he was there and quickly flew home.

When he returned, Perseus found that the evil king had imprisoned his mother, Danae. He went to the king's palace and challenged him to release his mother, telling him that he had killed the Gorgon. The king did not believe him and ordered him to show him the head. Perseus pulled the Gorgon's head from the bag, shielding his own eyes. The king stared at the face. Instantly, the king turned to solid stone. His surprised expression was frozen on his face for eternity.

The gods and goddesses were pleased with Perseus's showings of heroic qualities. Some versions of the myth say that he gave the head to Athene and that she put it in the middle of her shield.

Perseus and the Gorgons
Vocabulary Activities

Look up each word in the dictionary and write its definition.

Abducting:

Arid:

Brass:

Quest:

Ransom:

Cloak:

Fill in the blanks with a form of the correct vocabulary word from above.

1. The _____ in search of the magic sword was very dangerous.

2. His _____ was not as warm as his fitted jacket.

3. The man was arrested for _____ the woman and taking her out of state.

4. The area was an _____ desert.

5. The buttons were made of _____.

6. The kidnap victim was held for _____.

Use each vocabulary word in a sentence.

_____

_____

_____

_____

_____

_____

_____

_____

_____

Perseus and the Gorgons
Comprehension Questions

1. Why did Perseus go after Medusa?

_____

_____

_____

_____

2. Describe Medusa.

_____

_____

_____

_____

3. Who helped Perseus and what did they give him?

_____

_____

_____

_____

4. How did Perseus kill Medusa?

_____

_____

_____

5. What problem did he find when giving the evil king Medusa's head and how did he solve it?

_____

_____

_____

_____

Answers to "Perseus and the Gorgons"
Comprehension Questions and Vocabulary Exercises

Discussion Questions

1. Why did Perseus go after Medusa?

He was challenged by an evil king to bring back Medusa's head.

2. Describe Medusa.

She was one of three Gorgons. She was half dragon and half woman with scales on her body and hands of solid brass. Her hair was hundreds of poisonous snakes.

3. Who helped Perseus and what did they give him?

Athene and Hermes helped. They told Perseus to find the Graeae. The Graeae gave him winged sandals; the helmet of Hades to make him invisible; a sickle to decapitate Medusa; and a bag in which to put the head. Athene gave him her shield to reflect the image of Medusa.

4. How did Perseus kill Medusa?

He found her asleep and cut off her head.

5. What problem did he find when giving the evil king Medusa's head and how did he solve it?

The king had captured his mother and held her hostage. Perseus showed the king Medusa's head, which turned the evil king into stone.

Look up each word in the dictionary and write its definition.

Abducting: kidnapping

Arid: not having enough rainfall to support agriculture

Brass: an alloy containing copper and zinc

Quest: a journey towards a goal

Cloak: a long loose outer garment

Ransom: the release of property or a person in return for something

Fill in each sentence with the correct vocabulary word.

1. The <u>quest</u> in search of the magic sword was very dangerous.
2. His <u>cloak</u> was not as warm as his fitted jacket.
3. The man was arrested for <u>kidnapping</u> the woman and taking her out of state.
4. The area was an <u>arid</u> desert.
5. The buttons were made of <u>brass</u>.
6. The kidnap victim was held for <u>ransom</u>.

Perseus and the Gorgons
Creative-Thinking Questions

1. Do you think Perseus could have killed Medusa without the help of the gods and goddess? Why or why not?

_____

_____

_____

_____

2. Analyze why Perseus accepted the challenge.

_____

_____

_____

_____

3. Why, do you think, did the gods and goddess want to help Perseus? What did the gods and goddess do to show Perseus that they were pleased with him?

_____

_____

_____

_____

4. Suppose you had been Perseus. How might you have defeated Medusa without the help of the gods and goddesses?

_____

_____

_____

_____

5. What might have happened if the other Gorgons had awoken before Perseus had cut off Medusa's head?

_____

_____

_____

_____

6. Why would Perseus not look at the island where Medusa lived?

_____

_____

_____

_____

7. What do you think the king thought was in the bag?

_____

_____

_____

_____

8. Was the king's end fitting? Why or why not?

_____

_____

_____

_____

9. How do you think the other two Gorgons reacted when they found out what happened to Medusa? What became of them?

_____

_____

_____

_____

Perseus and the Gorgons
WHAT A HERO!

What do you think makes a modern day hero? Write about it.

Perseus and the Gorgons
SO YOU THINK YOU'RE SO SMART!

Suppose you had been Medusa.
How might you have outsmarted Perseus? Write about it.

Perseus and the Gorgons
YOU CAN LOOK NOW!

Design a way for people to look at Medusa's head without turning into stone.
Create a traveling show to make money showing off Medusa's head.
Tell how you would advertise the show.

Perseus and the Gorgons
ANOTHER ADVENTURE

Write about another adventure for Perseus.

Gods and Goddesses of Ancient Greece

Zeus: Supreme ruler of the gods and goddesses. He is lord of the sky and the rain god. His weapon is the thunderbolt.

Hera: Wife of Zeus. Queen of all the gods and goddesses. She is the protector of marriage and takes special care of married women. Her sacred animals are the cow and the peacock.

Poseidon: Brother of Zeus and Hades. Lord of the sea. His weapon is the trident. Some myths say he created the horse. He is second only to Zeus in power.

Hades: Brother of Zeus and Poseidon. Ruler of the dead and king of the Underworld. He is also god of wealth because of the precious metals mined from the earth. He has a helmet that makes him invisible.

Ares: Son of Zeus and Hera. He is the god of war. His bird is the vulture and his animal, the dog. He has a very murderous personality, yet he is a coward.

Athene: Daughter of Zeus. She is the patron goddess of Athens, handicrafts, and agriculture. She is known for her wisdom, reason and purity. Her tree is the olive; her bird is the owl.

Apollo: Son of Zeus and Leto. He is the god of music and plays a golden lyre. He is also the god of healing and taught man medicine. He is also the god of light and truth. He is known for shooting a silver bow. His tree was the laurel; his bird, the crow; and his animal, the dolphin.

Aphrodite: Daughter of Zeus and Dione. She is the goddess of love, desire and beauty. She has a magical girdle that makes men desire her. Her tree is the myrtle; her birds are the dove, the swan and the sparrow.

Artemis: Daughter of Zeus and Leto. She is the goddess of wild things and the huntress of the gods. She is also known as the protector of the young. She is associated with the moon. Like her brother, Apollo, she shoots silver arrows. Her tree is the cypress; all she is mistress of all wild animals, especially the deer.

Hephaestus: Son of Zeus and Hera. He is the god of fire and the forge. He is the patron god of both smiths and weavers. He is the only god to be physically ugly and deformed.

Research Unit Directions

Choose a god or goddess to research.

SOURCES
Choose three resources to use for your research. One of them may be an internet source.

BLOOM QUESTIONS
Read about Bloom's Taxonomy on pages 118–119. Using the template, write a Bloom question from each level based upon the mythology regarding your god or goddess to help you with your research. When you have completed the Bloom questions, you will begin your research.

NOTE CARDS
Not all the information in your resources will be important for your research. You will break the information down into categories, or topics, and record the important information onto note cards. This is a good way to get organized when working on a research topic.

Use a different color note card for each source. (If you don't have colored cards, you may use a sticker or a colored dot. The first card of each color should contain the bibliographic information. Each card within the color set will pertain to a particular category. Write a different category at the top of each card. (See pages 120–121.) As you do your research, you will put the information on your note cards.

BIBLIOGRAPHY
Create a bibliography of the sources you have used. (See page 122 for the proper format.)

OUTLINE
After completing your research using your three sources, use your note cards to organize the information into an outline. Each category on the note cards will become the Roman numerals for your outline. (See page 123 for an example of the outline.)

PRODUCT
After you complete your outline, you are ready to choose a product that will reflect your research. (See page 124 for product ideas.) Fill out a product proposal using the form on page 128. This will help you plan your product. When the product is finished, evaluate it by using the product evaluation form on page 125.

PRESENTATION
You are now ready to give their presentations. (See pages 126–127 for presentation tips.) Page 129 includes a scoring rubric that can be used to score the completed research project.

Levels of Bloom's Taxonomy

Benjamin Bloom divided educational questions into six main categories: knowledge, comprehension, application, analysis, synthesis and evaluation. The last four levels promote critical and creative thinking.

Level	_Skill Involved_
Knowledge:	simple recall
Comprehension:	understanding of the material
Application:	applying learned information to a new situation
Analysis:	the breaking down of learned knowledge into small parts
Synthesis:	creating something new and original from the acquired knowledge
Evaluation:	making a judgment and backing it up

The following verbs can help in writing Bloom questions.

Knowledge:	list, know, define, relate, repeat, recall, specify, tell, name
Comprehension:	recognize, restate, explain, describe, summarize, express, review, discuss, identify, locate, report, retell
Application:	demonstrate, interview, simulate, dramatize, experiment, show, use, employ, operate, exhibit, apply, calculate, solve, illustrate
Analysis:	compare, examine, categorize, group, test, inventory, probe, analyze, discover, arrange, organize, contrast, classify, survey
Synthesis:	plan, develop, invent, predict, propose, produce, arrange, formulate, construct, incorporate, originate, create, prepare, design, set up
Evaluation:	value, recommend, evaluate, criticize, estimate, decide, conclude, predict, judge, compare, rate, measure, select, infer

Bloom Questions

Knowledge
  1. List the parts of _____.
  2. Define how to _____.
  3. What does _____ mean?

Comprehension
  1. Describe how to _____.
  2. Explain how _____ happened.
  3. Locate where _____ is found.

Application
  1. Demonstrate how to _____.
  2. Tell how to operate a _____.
  3. Dramatize how _____ is different today.

Analysis
  1. Compare and contrast _____ and _____.
  2. How would you test _____?
  3. Organize _____ and test it.

Synthesis
  1. Plan a new way to _____.
  2. Create a new _____. Explain it.
  3. Design a way to _____.

Evaluation
  1. Judge the usefulness of _____.
  2. Predict how _____ may change _____.
  3. Recommend _____ to someone.

Note Cards and Organization

Use color-coded note cards. Put all the information from one source on cards of the same color. For example, all pink cards may refer to a certain book; all blue cards may come from an internet source; all white cards come from a magazine source; etc.

Make sure the first card of a color has the resource information. (See card No. 1.) **You can find this information on the title page and the reverse side of the title page.** Each note card should have a title or category describing what that card is about. (See Card No. 2.)

Card No. 1

> Caselli, Giovanni. Gods, Men and Monsters from Greek Mythology. New York: Peter Bedrick Books, 1977

Card No. 2

> Athene's Family
>
> Father: Zeus
>
> Mother: Metis

Bibliographies

A **bibliography** is a list of books and other sources of information. There are two main reasons to have a bibliography. First of all, it shows the research an author has done in preparing the work. It also tells readers where they can look if they want more information on the subject.

Each entry includes important information:

- Title of the Book
- Author's Name
- Name of Publisher
- Copyright Date

Entries are listed in alphabetical order. Alphabetical order is based on the first important word in the entry. Usually, that will be the author's last name. If an entry begins with a title, do not use the words "A," "An," or "The" to put the entries in order.

Bibliographies should be easy to read. Put a line space between each entry. Also, indent all lines in an entry except the first.

General Rules

Begin each entry at the left margin.

Indent all lines of an entry except the first.

Authors' names are written last name first.

If there are more than one author, write them in the same order as on the title page.

Alphabetize by the first important word in the entry. (Do not use "A," "An," or "The.")

Book and magazine titles should be printed in italics or underlined.

Tiles of articles in magazines are put in quotation marks.

Each entry should end with a period.

Skip a line between each entry.

Bibliography Formats

Follow the appropriate format for each type of resource. Be sure to notice the punctuation as well as the order of the information.

NOTE: If typed or handwritten, titles may be underlined instead of being done in italics. When no author is given, start with the name of the article.

Book Written by One Author:

Author's Last Name, Author's First Name. *Title of Book.* City Where Published: Publisher, Copyright Date.

Book Written by More Than One Author:

1st Author's Last Name, 1st Author's First Name, and 2nd Author's First and Last Name. (The rest is the same.)

If the same author has written more than one of the books, you may use a dash instead of the name. Alphabetize by the book title.

Encyclopedias and Other Reference Books:

Author's Last Name, Author's First Name (If known). "Title of Article." *Title of Reference Book.* Year of the Edition Used.

If you use an on-line encyclopedia, add the date you visited the site.

Magazines:

Author's Last Name, Author's First Name (If known). "Title of Article." *Magazine Name.* Date on Magazine: page(s).

World Wide Web:

Author's Last Name, Author's First Name (If known). "Title of Article." *Title of Work* (if there is one). Date you visited the site. <complete http address>.

Personal Interview:

Last Name, First Name. Personal Interview. Date Interviewed.

Outline Example

Athene

I. Birth
   A. Mother swallowed by Zeus
   B. Sprung from Zeus's head
      1. Arose in foamy water
      2. Dressed in full armor

II. Parents
   A. Father: Zeus
   B. Mother: Metis

III. Personality
   A. Wise
   B. Skillful at war
   C. Jealous

IV. Contributions to Mankind
   A. Taught man skills
      1. how to make the wheel
      2. axe
      3. flute and trumpet
      4. plow
      5. sail ships
      6. spin wool into thread and weave it into cloth
   B. Taught man could sometimes solve arguments by debate

V. Conflicts
   A. Arachne
      1. caused by jealousy
      2. destroyed tapestry
      3 turned her into spider
   B. Often took sides in conflicts between heroes

Product Ideas

diary

collection

puzzle

scrapbook

cartoon

invention

play

report

model

game

photograph display

teach a lesson

want ad

TV commercial

new theory

overhead transparency

display

story

brochure

mural

greeting card

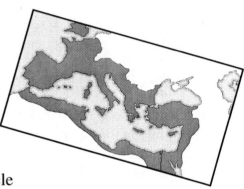

diagram

speech

book cover

audio tape

advertisement

poem

radio show

graph

map

diorama

magazine article

pop-up book

sculpture

new product

skit

flip book

secret code

newspaper article

puppet show

time line

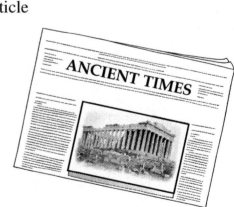

ANCIENT TIMES

Product Self-Evaluation

Are you pleased with your product? Why or why not?

_____

_____

_____

Do you think your product reflects your research? How?

_____

_____

_____

If you scored your product, 1 being the lowest and 10 being the highest, what score would you give it? Circle one.

1   2   3   4   5   6   7   8   9   10

Give some reasons why you scored your product as you did.

_____

_____

_____

Did you enjoy making your product? Why or why not?

_____

_____

_____

_____

Presentation Guidelines

Organize your presentation using the following outline. No matter what product you choose, you will have to present your information orally to the class. Use notes to help you present your research and your product.

I. Introduction
    A. Include a topic sentence.
    B. Be sure to grab your audience's attention.

II. Body
    A. This will be the major part of your presentation of your product.
    B. Include important information.
    C. Know your information so that you refer to your notes as little as possible.
    D. Show any visuals you have included.

III. Conclusion
    A. Summarize your presentation with one or two sentences.
    B. Do not include any new material.
    C. Ask for questions.

The topic or introductory sentence should "grab" your audiences' attention.

The body is your product presented.
- Do not read from your product.
- Know the information.
- Tell the class about what you learned.
- Show your product.

1. Know your topic and material well.
2. Be organized. Have your materials and information ready to use in your presentation.
3. Practice your presentation:
    • Do not read your presentation.
    • Give your presentation to anyone who will listen. Practice with your parents, your siblings, even your pets. The more often you give the presentation, the better and more comfortable you will become.
4. Make good eye contact with your audience.
5. Stand up straight, move a little, and don't stand in a frozen stance.
6. Use an oral presentation format:
    • Introduce your topic.
    • Explain each point you are trying to make.
    • Summarize your presentation with one or two sentences.
    • Ask if there are any questions.
7. Never turn your back on the audience.
8. Make sure your audience can hear you clearly.

Oral Presentation Tips

1. Know your topic and material well.

2. Be organized. Have your materials and information ready to use in your presentation.

3. Practice your presentation:

    • Do not read your presentation.

    • Give your presentation to anyone who will listen. Practice with your parents, your siblings, even your pets. The more often you give the presentation, the better and more comfortable you will become.

4. Make good eye contact with your audience.

5. Stand up straight, move a little, and don't stand in a frozen stance.

6. Use an oral presentation format:

    • Introduce your topic.

    • Explain each point you are trying to make.

    • Summarize your presentation with one or two sentences.

    • Ask if there are any questions.

7. Never turn your back on the audience.

8. Make sure your audience can hear you clearly.

    • Speak slowly so everyone can understand you.

Product Proposal

Name of Product: _____

Supplies needed to make the product:

_____   _____

_____   _____

_____   _____

_____   _____

_____   _____

Steps needed to make the product:

1._____

2._____

3._____

4._____

5._____

6._____

Did you have any problems?

_____

_____

_____

What could you do differently to make the product better?

_____

_____

_____

Research Project Grading

Name: _____

Resources: _____ (1-10 points)

___ Do you have three resources?

___ Is no more than one resource from the internet?

Note Cards: _____ (1-20 points)

___ Is the correct format used?

___ Is there no plagiarism?

___ Are the sources cited on the note cards?

Outline: _____ (1-10 points)

___ How well is the outline organized?

___ Does the outline reflect the research?

Research Presentation: _____ (1-30 points)

___ Was the audience attentive?

___ Did the presentation flow nicely?

___ Did the quality of ideas reflect higher-level thinking?

___ Did the conclusion summarize the research?

Bibliography: _____ (1-10 points)

___ Was the correct format used?

___ Were all the sources included?

Product: _____ (1-20 points)

___ Does the product reflect the research?

___ Is the product challenging?

___ Does the overall quality of product reflect hard work and careful research?

Bibliography

BOOKS

Bullfinch, Thomas. *A Book of Myths.* New York: Macmillan Publishing Company, 1980.

Carlile, Vowery. *Ready to Research Ancient Civilizations.* Hawthorne, NJ: Educational Impressions, Inc., 2006.

Caselli, Giovanni. *Gods, Men & Monsters from the Greek Myths.* New York: Peter Bedrick Books, 1977.

Hamilton, Edith. *Mythology.* New York: Little Brown and Company, 1998.

McAlpine, Jim and Marion Finkbinder, Sue Jeweler and Betty Weincek. *As It Was! Ancient Greece.* Hawthorne, NJ: Educational Impressions, Inc., 2001.

Stark, Rebecca. *Mythology.* Hawthorne, NJ: Educational Impressions, Inc., 2001.

VIDEOS

Timeless Tales: Myths of Ancient Greece, Set I. Hawthorne, NJ: Educational Impressions, Inc., 1979.

Timeless Tales: Myths of Ancient Greece, Set II. Hawthorne, NJ: Educational Impressions, Inc., 1986.